George Frideric Handel

Musick for the Royal Fireworks
HWV 351

Edited by / Herausgegeben von
Roger Fiske

EULENBURG

EAS 200
ISBN 978-3-7957-7701-2
ISMN 979-0-2002-2631-7

© 2016 Ernst Eulenburg & Co GmbH, Mainz
for Europe excluding the British Isles
Ernst Eulenburg Ltd, London
for all other countries
Edition based on Eulenburg Study Score ETP 1307
CD ℗ 2006 NAXOS Rights US, Inc.
CD © 2016 Ernst Eulenburg Ltd, London

Ernst Eulenburg Ltd
48 Great Marlborough Street
London W1F 7BB

Contents / Inhalt

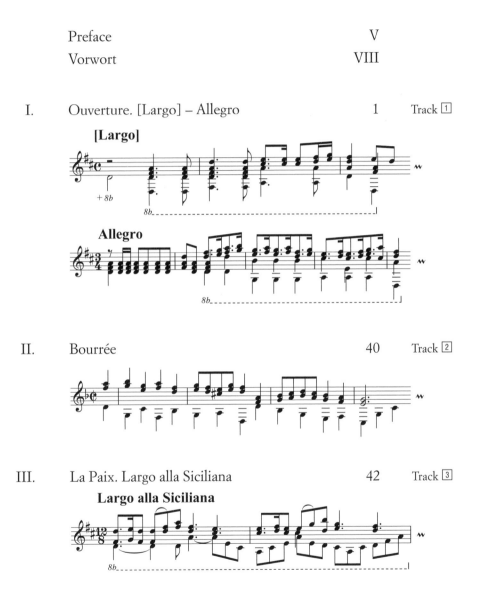

Preface

Composed: 1748/49
First performance: 27 April 1749 in London
Original Publisher: John Walsh, London, 1749
Versions and Arrangements: overture in two divergent forms as the basis for the wind version; for winds and kettledrums (military instruments); concert version for winds and strings
Orchestral Scoring: oboes I and II (twelve each), oboe III (four each) – horns I–III (three each), trumpets I–III (three each) – kettledrums – violins I and II, violas – basso continuo: bassoon I (eight each), bassoon II (four each), contrabassoon, cello, violone, harpsichord
Performance Duration: ca. 20 minutes

The Austrian War of Succession, smouldering since 1740 and triggering amongst other things disputes between France and England over hegemony in North American and Indian colonial territories, ended in October 1748 with the so-called 'treaty of Aix-la-Chapelle'. For England this peace involved compromises and concessions that did not arouse any real enthusiasm in the populace. The writer Horace Walpole noted: 'The Peace is signed between us, France and Holland, but does not give the least joy; the stocks do not rise, and the merchants are unsatisfied […] in short, there has not been the least symptom of public rejoicing; but the government is to give a magnificent fireworks.' Given the low morale, the fireworks display to celebrate the peace agreement, originally planned for October, was deferred until April 1749. This first of all gained time for an intensive propaganda campaign conducive to generating with the show the positive political impact desired – public approval of the peace treaty. In the months to follow, sufficient time also remained to erect in Green Park – then part of St James's Park in London – an elaborately designed stage construction in the form of a Doric temple that was to serve as the backdrop for the fireworks display. Pleasanter weather and a correspondingly large number of visitors were also anticipated with the postponement to April.

The show was to eclipse all previous fireworks displays. Appearing in the press were plans and reports of the monumental 'Green Park Machine' that the technicians from France and Italy planned and built. 10,000 pyrotechnical rockets were to be ignited, and glowing for five hours at the end was to be a sun with the inscription 'VIVAT REX' (Long Live the King). Amongst others participating in the fireworks display were members of a pyrotechnical dynasty from Bologna (the Ruggieri family) that would be in charge of the French Revolution celebrations four decades later and still be part of the centenary in 1986 to celebrate erecting the Statue of Liberty in New York.

That Handel was to provide the music for the fireworks display was made public in January 1749. Resident in London since 1710, he was considered since his naturalisation in 1727 England's greatest living composer. He had already contributed musical settings for a number of official occasions – his music seemed apposite as none other to lend the English royal house the desired sumptuous splendour.

Soon enough a dispute about the instrumentation flared up between Handel and the royal officials. According to a contemporaneous account the band was to include '40 trumpets, 20 horns, 16 oboes, 16 bassoons, 8 pairs of kettledrums, 12 side drums and a corresponding number of flutes and fifes' – military music of which obviously even King George II could approve, he who had originally not wanted to commission any music at all for the fireworks display. Yet, such a scoring was of course utterly unrealistic – the sound of 16 oboes playing together with 40 trumpets would be totally lost. Handel would probably also have realised that such a large number of qualified military musicians who could have read and rehearsed his music was unlikely to be fulfilled – military musicians normally played from memory. He might even have felt little inclined to produce a work for such a large and unusual a scoring, as it offered hardly any possibility of repeat performance, and a printed edition would therefore have not promised any commercial success. But in reality he himself had already agreed to a charity concert in the Foundling Hospital for May 1749, at which he wanted once again to perform the music. For this occasion he had planned a string set-up that he had already notated in the appropriate places in the score. He now spared no effort to give the composition a shape in line with his wishes and needs and even threatened to cancel the entire project. His strategy was successful mostly because no other composer was available to fulfil this compositional commission – and Handel well appreciated this.

There was also discussion of a public dress rehearsal in Vauxhall Gardens. Handel initially objected to this plan – not only for logistical reasons concerning the installation of the large orchestral set-up, but probably first and foremost because admission to the dress rehearsal would not be free and therefore this would rank as a regular production. Hence, the music would no longer be a novelty at the official fireworks production, and even its presentation at the charity concert would thereby lose its attraction. But this time Handel could not have his own way and ultimately had to bow to the plan of a public dress rehearsal on 21 April 1749. It turned out to be an unparalleled crowd-puller. Even though the attendance number of 12,000 making the rounds of contemporary press accounts was probably immoderately exaggerated, nevertheless so many people streamed into the gardens that they caused a three-hours-long traffic jam on London Bridge, the only possible road access south to Vauxhall.

Astonishingly, no detailed report of Handel's music is extant despite the high attendance numbers. The same is true for the day of the official fireworks taking place on 27 April in Green Park, likewise before the eyes of thousands of spectators. That at the extravaganza the music turned out to be so much in the background probably had to do with the fact that the fireworks ended in a disaster. Part of the wooden stage construction caught fire, and the firefighters standing by as a precaution could only with difficulty prevent a spread to the complete facility.

At any rate, a look at the autograph score can hardly convey an impression of the scoring in which Handel ultimately presented the fireworks music at Green Park: here he notated 24 oboes, 12 bassoons, 9 horns, 9 trumpets and 3 pairs of kettledrums. In the same score he also entered the orchestration variants with strings planned for the Foundling Hospital concert.

The *Fireworks Music* is not only Handel's last instrumental work, but also the most extensive of all his instrumental works. Its musical splendour feeds on an idiom especially festive melodically and striking harmonically, with terse rhythms. Handel borrowed the musical material of the six movements from several of his own and others' works and put it together afresh – a practice that he frequently resorted to in his compositions. In the overture, by far the longest movement of the work, he used music from two concertos that he had written as interlude music for oratorio performances. Musical motifs in 'La Paix' show affinity with Telemann's *Tafelmusik*, material rearranged in 'La Réjouissance' is from an opera by Giovanni Porta. Handel extracted the second minuet from his own *Occasional Oratorio* of 1746.

Susanne Schaal-Gotthardt
Translation: Margit L. McCorkle

Vorwort

komponiert: 1748/49
Uraufführung: 27. April 1749 in London
Originalverlag: John Walsh, London, 1749
Fassungen und Bearbeitungen: Ouvertüre in zwei voneinander abweichenden Formen als Basis für die Bläserfassung; für Bläser und Pauken (Militärinstrumente); Konzertfassung für Bläser und Streicher
Orchesterbesetzung: Oboe I und II (je zwölffach), Oboe III (vierfach) – Horn I–III (je dreifach), Trompete I–III (je dreifach) – Pauken – Violinen I und II, Bratschen – Basso continuo: Fagott I (achtfach), Fagott II (vierfach), Kontrafagott, Violoncello, Violone, Cembalo
Spieldauer: etwa 20 Minuten

Der seit 1740 schwelende Österreichische Erbfolgekrieg, der unter anderem Auseinandersetzungen zwischen Frankreich und England um die Vorherrschaft in Koloniegebieten Nordamerikas und Indiens ausgelöst hatte, endete im Oktober 1748 mit dem sogenannten „Frieden von Aachen". Für England war dieser Frieden mit Kompromissen und Zugeständnissen verbunden, die in der Bevölkerung keine rechte Begeisterung aufkommen lassen wollten. Der Schriftsteller Horace Walpole stellte fest: „Der Frieden zwischen uns, Frankreich und Holland wurde unterzeichnet, er ist aber nicht im mindesten erfreulich; die Aktien steigen nicht, und die Kaufleute sind unzufrieden [...] kurz gesagt, es hat nicht das leiseste Anzeichen von öffentlicher Freude gegeben; die Regierung wird aber ein prächtiges Feuerwerk veranstalten." Angesichts der schlechten Stimmung wurde das ursprünglich noch für Oktober geplante Feuerwerk, mit dem der Friedensschluss gefeiert werden sollte, auf den April 1749 verschoben. Damit war vor allem Zeit für eine intensive Propaganda gewonnen, die dazu beitragen sollte, dass das Spektakel auch die gewünschte positive politische Wirkung erzielte – die öffentliche Zustimmung zum Friedensvertrag. Auch blieb in den folgenden Monaten genügend Zeit, um im Green Park – damals Teil des Londoner St. James's Park – eine aufwendig gestaltete Bühnenkonstruktion in Form eines dorischen Tempels zu errichten, die als Kulisse für das Feuerwerk dienen sollte. Mit der Verlegung in den April erhoffte man sich außerdem freundlichere Wetterverhältnisse und eine entsprechend große Besucherzahl.

Das Schauspiel sollte bisherige Feuerwerke in den Schatten stellen. In der Presse erschienen Pläne und Berichte von der monumentalen „Green Park Machine", die Techniker aus Frankreich und Italien planten und erbauten. 10.000 Feuerwerksraketen sollten gezündet werden, und am Ende sollte eine Sonne mit der Inschrift „VIVAT REX" (Es lebe der König) für fünf Stunden lang glühen. An dem Feuerwerk waren unter anderem Mitglieder einer Pyrotechnikerdynastie aus Bologna (die Familie Ruggieri) beteiligt, die vier Jahrzehnte später das Feuerwerk für die Feierlichkeiten der Französischen Revolution betreute und noch 1986 bei der Hundertjahrfeier zur Errichtung der New Yorker Freiheitsstatue mitwirkte.

Dass Händel die Musik für das Feuerwerksspektakel liefern sollte, wurde im Januar 1749 publik. Händel, der seit 1710 in London lebte, galt seit seiner Einbürgerung 1727 als der größte lebende englische Komponist. Zu etlichen offiziellen Anlässen hatte er schon die musikalische Umrahmung beigesteuert – wie keine andere schien seine Musik dazu geeignet, dem englischen Königshaus den gewünschten prunkvollen Glanz zu verleihen.

Über die Instrumentierung des Stücks entbrannte schon bald ein Disput zwischen Händel und den königlichen Beamten. Nach einem zeitgenössischen Bericht sollte die Kapelle mit „40 Trompeten, 20 Hörnern, 16 Oboen, 16 Fagotten, 8 Paar Pauken, 12 Kleinen Trommeln und einer entsprechenden Anzahl von Flöten und Querpfeifen" besetzt werden – eine Militärmusik, mit der offenkundig auch König Georg II. einverstanden war, der ursprünglich überhaupt keine Musik zum Feuerwerk hatte bestellen wollen. Doch natürlich war eine solche Instrumentierung völlig unrealistisch – im Zusammenspiel mit 40 Trompeten gehen 16 Oboen klanglich komplett verloren. Händel dürfte sich darüber hinaus im Klaren darüber gewesen sein, dass eine solch große Anzahl von musikalisch geschulten Militärmusikern, die seine Noten hätten lesen und einstudieren können, gar nicht zur Verfügung stand – Militärmusiker musizierten für gewöhnlich auswendig. Auch dürfte er wenig Neigung verspürt haben, ein Werk für eine derart große und ungewöhnliche Besetzung anzufertigen, da sich kaum je eine Möglichkeit zur Wiederaufführung geboten und deshalb auch eine gedruckte Ausgabe keinen kommerziellen Erfolg versprochen hätte. Tatsächlich hatte er selbst aber schon für Mai 1749 ein Wohltätigkeitskonzert im Foundling Hospital verabredet, bei dem er die Musik nochmals aufführen wollte. Für diesen Anlass hatte er einen Streicherapparat vorgesehen, den er an den entsprechenden Stellen in der Partitur auch schon notiert hatte. Er setzte nun alles daran, der Komposition eine Gestalt zu geben, die seinen Wünschen und Bedürfnissen entsprach, und drohte sogar mit einer Absage des ganzen Projekts. Seine Strategie hatte Erfolg, vor allem auch deshalb, weil kein anderer Komponist für die Erfüllung dieses Kompositionsauftrags zur Verfügung stand – und Händel war sich dessen wohl bewusst.

Diskussionen gab es auch um eine öffentliche Generalprobe in Vauxhall Gardens. Händel lehnte diesen Plan zunächst ab – nicht nur aus logistischen Gründen wegen der Installierung des großen Orchesterapparats, sondern wohl vor allem deshalb, weil der Besuch der Generalprobe Eintritt kostete und diese damit den Rang einer regulären Veranstaltung erhielt. Damit wäre die Musik aber bei der offiziellen Feuerwerksveranstaltung keine Novität mehr, und auch ihre Präsentation beim Wohltätigkeitskonzert im Foundling Hospital verlöre dadurch an Attraktivität. Doch diesmal konnte sich Händel nicht durchsetzen und beugte sich schließlich dem Plan einer öffentlichen Generalprobe am 21. April 1749. Sie entpuppte sich als Publikumsmagnet sondergleichen. Selbst wenn die Zahl von 12.000 Besuchern, die in den zeitgenössischen Presseberichten kursierte, maßlos übertrieben sein dürfte, strömten doch so viele Menschen in den Park, dass sie einen dreistündigen Stau auf der London Bridge verursachten, dem einzig möglichen Zufahrtsweg südlich von Vauxhall.

Erstaunlicherweise hat sich trotz der hohen Besucherzahlen kein detaillierter Bericht zu Händels Musik erhalten. Gleiches gilt für den Tag des offiziellen Feuerwerks, das am 27. April in Green Park unter den Augen von ebenfalls tausenden von Zuschauern stattfand. Dass die Musik bei dem Spektakel so in den Hintergrund geriet, lag wohl auch daran, dass das Feuerwerk in einem Desaster endete. Ein Teil des hölzernen Bühnenbaus geriet in Brand, und nur mit Mühe konnten die vorsorglich bereitstehenden Feuerwehrleute ein Übergreifen auf die komplette Anlage verhindern.

Zumindest der Blick in die autographe Partitur kann einen Eindruck davon vermitteln, in welcher Besetzung Händel die Feuerwerksmusik in Green Park schließlich präsentierte: hier notierte er 24 Oboen, 12 Fagotte, 9 Hörner, 9 Trompeten und 3 Paar Kesselpauken. In dieselbe Partitur hat er auch die Besetzungsvariante mit Streichern eingetragen, die für das Konzert im Foundling Hospital vorgesehen war.

Die *Feuerwerksmusik* ist nicht nur Händels letztes, sondern auch sein umfangreichstes Instrumentalwerk überhaupt. Ihre musikalische Pracht speist sich aus einer besonders festlichen Melodik, plakativer Harmonik und prägnanten Rhythmen. Musikalisches Material der sechs Sätze hat Händel aus mehreren eigenen und fremden Werken entlehnt und neu zusammengestellt – eine Praxis, die er in seinen Kompositionen häufig anwandte. In der Ouvertüre, dem mit Abstand ausgedehntesten Satz der Komposition, verwendete er Musik aus zwei Konzerten, die er als Zwischenaktmusiken für Oratorienaufführungen geschrieben hatte. Musikalische Motive im Satz „La Paix" zeigen Verwandtschaft mit Telemanns „Tafelmusik", in „La Réjouissance" ist Material aus einer Oper des Italieners Giovanni Porta verarbeitet. Das zweite Menuett entnahm Händel seinem eigenen „Occasional Oratorio" aus dem Jahr 1746.

Susanne Schaal-Gotthardt

Musick for the Royal Fireworks

I. Ouverture

George Frideric Handel
(1685–1759)
HWV 351

EAS 200

Edited by Roger Fiske
© 2016 Ernst Eulenburg Ltd, London
and Ernst Eulenburg & Co GmbH, Mainz

2

6

Allegro

18

Lentement

Da capo $\frac{3}{4}$ fine al segno $\frown$

[bb47–117]

40

II. Bourrée 2 fois

La seconda volta senza Hautb. e Bassons

III. La Paix

Largo alla Siciliana

Corno 1
for 3 persons

Corno 2
for 3 persons

Corno 3
for 3 persons

Oboe 1
for 12 persons
e Violino I

Oboe 2
for 12 persons
e Violino II

Bassons
Vc. e Cb.

Viola colli Bassi

Cor. 2

Ob. 1
(Vl. I)

Ob. 2
(Vl. II)

Bsn.
Vc. e Cb.

44

IV. La Réjouissance

Allegro

With the Side Drum

48

The second time *by the French Horns and Hautbois and Bassons*
without Trumpets and Kettle Drums

The third time *all together*

EAS 200

V. Menuet [I] 2 fois

Menuet [II]

La seconda volta *colli* Corni da Caccia, Hautbois et Bassons
La terza volta *tutti insieme and the Side Drums*

Printed in China

THE ART OF SCORE-READING

The first steps

A score contains the entire musical text of a musical work in order that the conductor and everyone who wants to study the piece more thoroughly can see exactly which passages are being played by the orchestra or ensemble. The parts of the individual instruments are arranged in such a way that all notes played at the same time are written one below the other.

Scores help us to listen to, understand and interpret musical works. Those who only listen to music are unaware of many important details which, after some practice, become apparent when reading the score while listening to the music. The clear structure of the score helps to easily understand the compositional style and the characteristic features of a piece – this is a prerequisite not only for any analysis but also for the musician's own performance and interpretation.

The simplest method of score-reading is to read an individual part by concentrating on an individual part that can be heard particularly well. The most suitable pieces to begin with are concertos with solo instruments such as Beethoven's Romance in F major for violin and orchestra (example 1) or orchestral songs (with them, one may easily follow the text). Furthermore, in many classical orchestral works, it is quite easy to follow the lead part of the principal violin, or the bass part in baroque compositions for orchestra.

The next step is to try to change from one part to another and vice versa and follow the part that is leading. Little by little, you learn to find distinctive parts you hear in the score as well and follow them in the corresponding staff. This can be very easily tried out with Beethoven's Symphony No. 5 (example 2). To read the score, it is also helpful to count the bars. This technique is rather useful in the case of confusing or complex scores, such as those of contemporary music, and is particularly suitable when you do not want to lag behind in any case. It should be your aim, however, to eventually give up counting the bars and to read the score by first following individual parts and then going over to section-by-section or selective reading (see next page).

Example 1 · from: Romance for violin and orchestra in F major by Beethoven

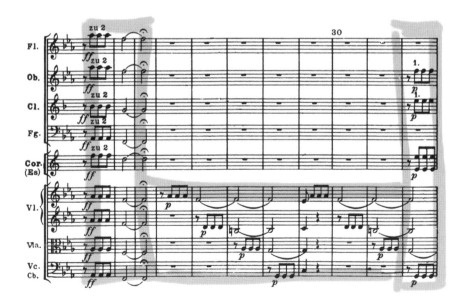

Example 2 · from: Symphony No. 5 C-minor by Beethoven

Further score-reading techniques

Example 3 · from: Symphony No. 100 G major 'Military' by Haydn

Example 4 · from: Symphony No. 41 C major 'Jupiter' by W. A. Mozart

Section-by-section reading

This technique is suitable for application in the 'Military' Symphony by Haydn (example 3). In bb. 260-264, the parts are mostly in parallel motion so that it is quite easy to take in the section as a whole. In the strings, the texture is homophonic (i.e. all instruments play the same rhythm), consisting of tone repetitions in the lower parts while there is a little more movement in the part of the first violin. At the same time, the tones of the winds are stationary (i.e. long sustained notes), serving as harmonic filling-in. If need be, they can also be read en bloc.

Such block-like structures often consist of unison figures (= all instruments play the same), such as at the beginning of Mozart's Jupiter Symphony (example 4). Here, the score-reading can first be limited to the strings section which carries the melody alone in bb. 3-4 and contains all important information.

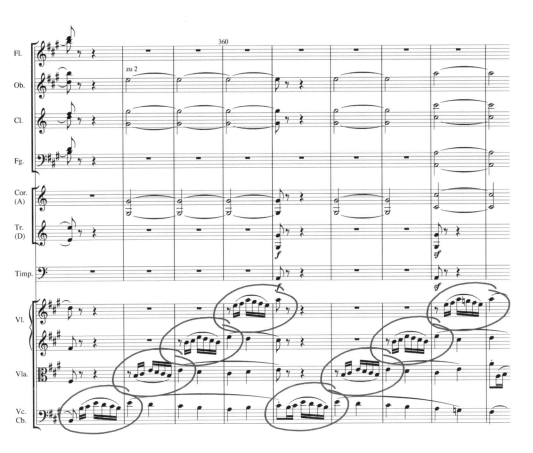

Example 5 · from: Symphony No. 7 A major by Beethoven

Selective reading

Using this technique, you concentrate on selected parts (lead parts, conspicuous passages) in the score. In the excerpt from Beethoven's Symphony No. 7 (example 5), it is the semiquaver motif that, originating with the violoncellos and basses and pervading the string parts twice, is particularly well suited. The stationary tones of the winds, consisting only of the note E in various octave positions in bb. 358-363, form the harmonic foundation and play a subordinate role in score-reading. Though they are briefly noticed, it is the strings and especially the conspicuous semiquaver motif pervading the individual parts that are to be followed.

With both score-reading techniques which should be chosen according to the nature of the passage in question, it is not important in the beginning to be able to follow at once all tones and harmonies. What matters more is to recognize and comprehend sequences of movement. Everything else comes with experience.

Following contrapuntal parts

The present excerpt from Brahms's Requiem (example 6) is polyphonic, i.e. one has to be able to follow several equal parts either alternately (without lagging behind) or simultaneously. But by looking for parallel parts in the score, the notation which, at first glance, seems to be overcrowded soon becomes clearer. For example, Brahms allocates orchestral parts to each choral part. As a consequence, there are many parts written in the score but considerably fewer independent parts actually played. Hence, the large amount of written music can be reduced to a manageable quantity.

The flute, clarinet, first violins and soprano are in parallel motion. Furthermore, the tenor of oboe and viola is supported by a much-expanded, yet parallel part.
The violoncellos and bassoons too are in almost parallel motion.

The low winds and strings as well as the timpani played simultaneously with the polyphonic parts are fill-in parts which consist only of stationary tones (sustained notes). They do not need to be followed upon first reading of the score.

Seen as a whole, this excerpt is most suitable for focussing on the soprano voice as it is coupled with two instruments and, being the highest voice, can be heard very well. In addition, the text is an aid to orientation, making it easier to return from brief trips to other parts.

In fugal sections, score-reading will be easier if the entries of the theme in the score are first looked for and then marked.

Example 6 · from: A German Requiem by Brahms

The score at a glance

A **Bar lines** are solid vertical lines within the instrument sections.

B The **bar numbers** are an aid to orientation in the score. Sometimes capital letters, so-called rehearsal letters, are used instead of numbers.

C The system of parallel lines on and between which the notes are written is called **staff** (or stave). The instrument abbreviation in front of each line (here, Fl. is for 'flute') indicates to which instrument(s) the line(s) refer(s).

D The **barline at the left-hand end** of the staves connects all staves to form the **system**.

E In addition to the barline at the left-hand end of the staves, **angular brackets** connect the individual groups of instruments in a score (wind, brass and string instruments). Within these groups, the instruments are arranged according to their pitch, with the highest-pitched instrument mentioned first.
Today, the common order of instrumental parts in the score is as follows, from top to bottom:
· wind instruments
· brass instruments
· percussion instruments
· harp, piano, celesta
· solo instrument(s)
· solo voices
· choir
· string instruments

F When there are two systems on a page, they are separated from each other by two parallel **diagonal strokes**.

G Instruments the names of which are followed by 'in Bb' or (Bb) are **transposing instruments**. In this case, (Bb) indicates that the notated C is played as Bb, i.e. all tones are played a tone lower than notated. Most of the transposing instruments are easily recognizable in the score thanks to these additions. However, there are also transposing instruments without such indications in the score, such as:
· piccolo flute (in C / an octave higher)
· cor anglais (in F / a fifth lower)
· contrabassoon (in C / an octave lower)
· double bass (in C / an octave lower)

H The transposing brass instruments have no general signature but, if need be, accidentals preceding the respective tone.

I The viola part is notated in the **alto clef**, the parts of violoncello and bassoon sometimes in the **tenor clef**. Both clefs are easy to read when the player realizes that the clef frames the note C1:
alto clef   tenor clef   treble clef

J Any change of key or time is marked by a **double bar**. The alla-breve sign following in this example (¢), like the sign for four-four time (c), is a relic from an old notational practice and stands for two-two time.

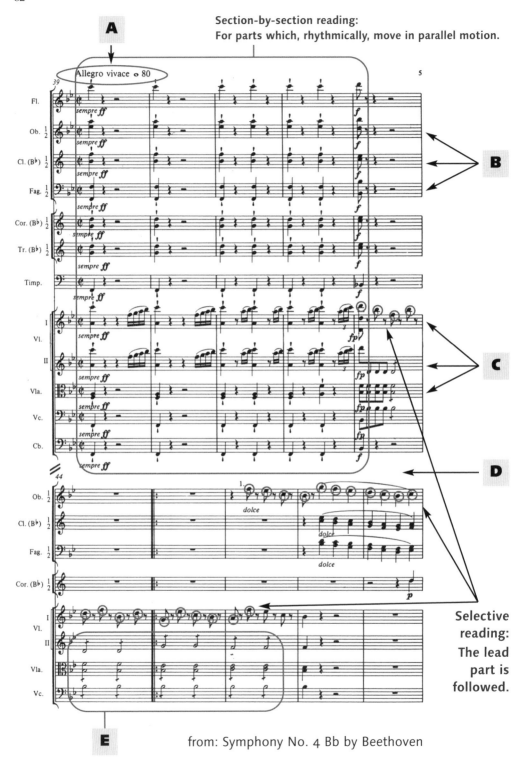

Section-by-section reading:
For parts which, rhythmically, move in parallel motion.

Selective reading:
The lead part is followed.

from: Symphony No. 4 Bb by Beethoven

A **Tempo indications** (sometimes in connection with metronome markings) are used by the composer to indicate how fast a piece shall be played.

B In the winds, two parts are usually brought together in one line. If they play the same note, the note head either has two stems or 'a2' written above it.

C Two-part chords in the staves of the strings are played by one player. If the parts shall be divided, **divisi** (divided) is written in the score. Then, at each desk, one player plays the upper notes and another player the lower notes.

D When an instrumental part contains a long rest, as in this flute part for example, its staff is often omitted until the next entry of the instrument, thus saving space. In addition, there are less page-turns, and the playing parts are arranged much clearer.

E In order to save space and arrange phrases or groups of notes more clearly, so-called abbreviations are used occasionally. The sign ♩ stands for ♪♪♪♪, with the minim indicating the duration of the repetitions and the stroke crossing the stem indicating the value of the notes to be repeated (1 stroke = quaver, 2 strokes = semiquaver, etc.). Cf. also the viola in b. 43 in which the repeated notes are first written out and then abbreviated.

Score-Reading with pupils and students!

Order this guideline for score-reading for your class! The leaflet 'The Art of Score-Reading' is available separately or as a set of copies and can be obtained free of charge while stock last.

Brochure 'The Art of Score-Reading'
Order No. ETP 9998-99 (free of charge)

Mozart for the classroom

A picture of life and travel

Mozart was not only one of the greatest composers, but also one of the best pianists of the 18th century. Like the virtous of today, he spent a large part of his life on concert tours at the leading courts and great cities of his time.

This small brochure depicts a panorama of the musical life in Europe wich formed the background to Mozart's oeuvre. The picture is completed by a short biography and a little insight into his way of composing.

Brochure 'Mozart. A Picture of Life and Travel'
Order No. ETP 9991-99 (free of charge)

For further information, see at: www.eulenburg.de

Eulenburg

DIE KUNST
DES PARTITURLESENS

Der erste Einstieg

Eine Partitur enthält den gesamten Notentext eines Musikwerkes, damit der Dirigent und jeder, der sich näher mit dem Stück beschäftigen will, genau nachvollziehen kann, was das Orchester oder das Ensemble spielt. Dabei sind die Instrumente so angeordnet, dass alle Noten, die zur gleichen Zeit erklingen, genau untereinander stehen.

Partituren helfen beim Hören, Begreifen und Interpretieren von Musikliteratur. Wer nur zuhört, erkennt viele kostbare Kleinigkeiten nicht, die beim Mitlesen nach ein wenig Übung regelrecht sichtbar werden. Der Kompositionsstil und die Charakteristik eines Werkes lassen sich mit der übersichtlichen Partitur schnell begreifen – das ist nicht nur Grundvoraussetzung für jede Analyse, sondern auch für das eigene Spiel.

Die einfachste Methode beim Partiturlesen ist das Verfolgen einer Einzelstimme. Bei diesem Verfahren konzentriert man sich auf eine einzelne Stimme, die besonders gut zu hören ist. Zum Einstieg eignen sich dabei besonders gut Konzerte mit Soloinstrumenten wie die Romanze in F-Dur für Violine und Orchester von Beethoven (Beispiel 1) oder Orchesterlieder (bei letzteren kann man sich leicht am Text orientieren). Weiterhin kann man bei vielen klassischen Orchesterwerken die führende Stimme der ersten Violine gut verfolgen, sowie bei barocken Kompositionen für Orchester die Bass-Stimme.

In einem nächsten Schritt kann man versuchen, zwischen den Stimmen zu wechseln und jeweils die Stimme zu verfolgen, die gerade führend ist. Nach und nach lernt man dabei markante Stimmen, die man hört, auch in der Partitur zu finden und im entsprechenden Notensystem zu verfolgen. Besonders anschaulich kann man das mittels Beethovens 5. Symphonie erproben (Beispiel 2).

Eine weitere Hilfe beim Lesen der Partitur kann auch das Mitzählen der Takte sein. Dieses Verfahren hilft bei unübersichtlichen oder komplexen Partituren wie etwa zeitgenössischer Musik und eignet sich besonders, wenn man den Anschluss auf keinen Fall verlieren möchte. Ziel sollte es jedoch sein, das Mitzählen der Takte gänzlich zu verlassen und die Partitur zunächst anhand einzelner Stimmen und dann im Wechsel von blockweisem bzw. selektivem Lesen zu verfolgen (siehe nächste Seite).

Beispiel 1 · aus: Romanze für Violine und Orchester F-Dur von Beethoven

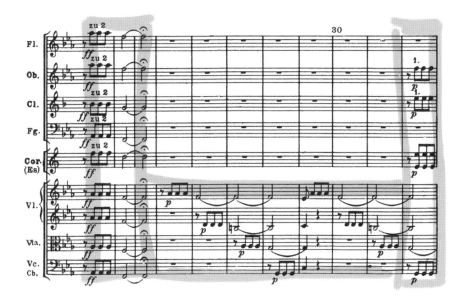

Beispiel 2 · aus: Symphonie Nr. 5 c-moll von Beethoven

Weitere Methoden des Partiturlesens

Beispiel 3 · aus: Symphonie Nr. 100 G-Dur „Militär" von Haydn

Beispiel 4 · aus: Symphonie Nr. 41 C-Dur „Jupiter" von W. A. Mozart

Blockweises Lesen

Diese Methode bietet sich in der Militär-Symphonie von Haydn an (Beispiel 3). In den T. 260-264 sind die Stimmen weitgehend parallel geführt, so dass man sie gut im Ganzen überblicken kann. In den Streichern haben wir einen homophonen Satz (d.h. alle Stimmen spielen den gleichen Rhythmus), der in den unteren Stimmen aus Tonwiederholungen besteht, während die erste Violine etwas bewegter ist. Gleichzeitig erklingen in den Bläserstimmen Liegetöne (d.h. lang ausgehaltene Töne), die als harmonischer Füllstoff dienen. Sie können bei Bedarf auch im Block gelesen werden.

Oft bestehen solche blockhaften Gebilde auch aus unisono-Figuren (= alle Stimmen spielen dasselbe), wie z.B. am Beginn der Jupiter-Symphonie von Mozart (Beispiel 4). Hier kann man sich beim Lesen zunächst nur auf den Streicherblock beschränken, der in den T. 3-4 alleine die Melodie weiterführt und bereits alle wichtigen Informationen enthält.

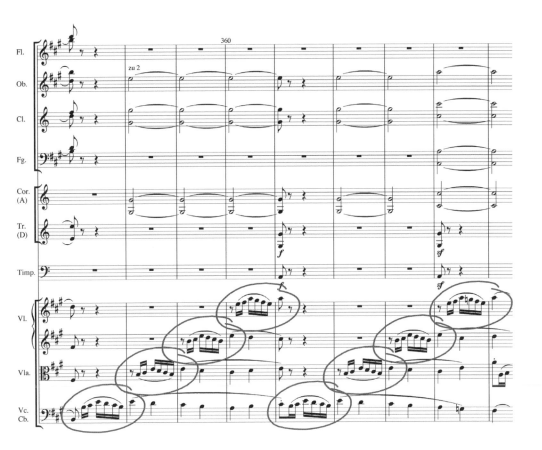

Beispiel 5 · aus: Symphonie Nr. 7 A-Dur von Beethoven

Selektives Lesen

Bei dieser Methode orientiert man sich anhand ausgewählter Stimmen (führende Stimmen, auffällige Stellen) in der Partitur. Im Ausschnitt aus Beethovens 7. Symphonie (Beispiel 5) ist hierzu das Sechzehntelmotiv geeignet, das zweimal von den Celli und Bässen ausgehend durch die Streicherstimmen wandert. Die Liegetöne der Bläser, die in den T. 358-363 sogar nur aus dem Ton e in unterschiedlichen Oktavlagen bestehen, bilden die harmonische Grundierung und spielen beim Lesen der Partitur eine untergeordnete Rolle. Man nimmt sie kurz wahr, verfolgt jedoch die Streicher und dort insbesondere das auffällige Sechzehntelmotiv in seiner Wanderung durch die einzelnen Stimmen.

Bei beiden Leseformen, zwischen denen man übrigens je nach Beschaffenheit der Stelle wechseln sollte, kommt es am Anfang nicht darauf an, sofort alle Töne und Harmonien verfolgen zu können. Viel wichtiger ist es, Bewegungsabläufe zu erkennen und nachzuvollziehen. Alles Weitere kommt mit der Erfahrung.

Verfolgen von kontrapunktischen Stimmen

Der vorliegende Ausschnitt aus Brahms' Requiem (Beispiel 6) ist polyphon komponiert, d.h. man muss mehrere gleichwertige Stimmen entweder im Wechsel (ohne den Anschluss zu verlieren) oder gleichzeitig verfolgen können.

Doch das auf den ersten Blick so übervolle Notenbild lichtet sich bald, wenn man sich die Partitur näher auf parallele Stimmen ansieht. Brahms ordnet z.B. jeder Chorstimme Orchesterstimmen zu. Das hat zur Folge, dass hier zwar viele Stimmen notiert sind, aber wesentlich weniger eigenständige Stimmen tatsächlich erklingen. Die vielen geschriebenen Noten lassen sich also auf ein überschaubares Maß reduzieren.

So werden Flöte, Klarinette, erste Violinen und Sopran parallel geführt. Des Weiteren wird der Tenor von Oboe und Bratsche mit einer stark erweiterten, aber dennoch parallel verlaufenden Stimme unterstützt. Ebenfalls fast ganz parallel verlaufen Violoncelli und Fagotte.

Zu den polyphon gefügten Stimmen erklingen die tiefen Bläser und Streicher sowie die Pauke mit Füllstimmen, welche lediglich aus Liegetönen (ausgehaltene Töne) bestehen. Sie braucht man beim ersten Lesen nicht weiter zu verfolgen.

Im Ganzen gesehen bietet sich in diesem Ausschnitt an, schwerpunktmäßig die Sopranstimme zu verfolgen, da sie mit zwei Instrumenten gekoppelt ist und als höchste Stimme gut herauszuhören ist. Zudem bietet der Text eine Orientierungshilfe, so dass der Wiedereinstieg von vorübergehenden Ausflügen in andere Stimmen erleichtert wird.

Bei fugierten Abschnitten kann man sich das Mitlesen auch erleichtern, indem man zunächst alle Einsätze des Themas in der Partitur sucht und sich markiert.

Beispiel 6 · aus: Ein deutsches Requiem von Brahms

Die Partitur im Überblick

A **Taktstriche** sind innerhalb der Instrumentengruppen durchgezogen.

B Die **Taktzahlen** erleichtern die Orientierung in der Partitur. Manchmal dienen hierzu auch Großbuchstaben, sog. Studierbuchstaben.

C Eine einzelne Zeile der Partitur nennt man **Notensystem**. Für welche(s) Instrument(e) sie steht, zeigt der **Instrumentenvorsatz** an (hier Fl. für Flöte).

D Der **Kopfstrich** verbindet alle Notensysteme miteinander zu einer **Akkolade**.

E Zusätzlich zum Kopfstrich fassen **gerade Klammern** die einzelnen Instrumentengruppen (Holz-, Blech- und Streichinstrumente) zusammen. Innerhalb dieser Gruppen sind die Instrumente nach Tonlage geordnet, wobei das höchste an oberster Stelle steht.
Die heute übliche Partituranordnung lautet von oben nach unten:
· Holzblasinstrumente
· Blechblasinstrumente
· Schlaginstrumente
· Harfe, Klavier, Celesta
· Soloinstrument(e)
· Solostimmen
· Chor
· Streichinstrumente

F Stehen zwei Akkoladen auf einer Seite, werden sie durch zwei **Schrägstriche** voneinander abgetrennt.

G Steht hinter dem Instrumentennamen z.B. „in B" oder (B), handelt es sich um ein **transponierendes Instrument**. In diesem Fall deutet das (B) an, dass das notierte C als B erklingt, also alle Noten einen Ton tiefer erklingen als sie notiert sind. Die meisten transponierenden Instrumente sind in der Partitur durch diese Zusätze leicht zu erkennen. Es gibt aber auch transponierende Instrumente ohne eine entsprechende Angabe in der Partitur, wie z.B.:
Piccoloflöte (in c/eine Oktave höher)
Englischhorn (in f/eine Quinte tiefer)
Kontrafagott (in c/eine Oktave tiefer)
Kontrabass (in c/eine Oktave tiefer)

H Die transponierenden Blechblasinstrumente haben keine Generalvorzeichen, sondern bei Bedarf Versetzungszeichen, die direkt vor der jeweiligen Note stehen.

I Die Viola oder Bratsche wird im **Alt- bzw. Bratschenschlüssel** notiert, die Stimmen des Violoncellos und Fagotts manchmal im **Tenorschlüssel**. Beide Schlüssel sind leicht zu lesen, wenn man sich klarmacht, dass der Schlüssel den Ton c1 umrahmt, also:

Alt-   Tenor-   Violinschlüssel

J Vor einem Wechsel der Ton- oder Taktart steht immer ein **Doppelstrich**. Das hier folgende Alla-Breve-Zeichen (¢) ist ebenso wie das Zeichen für den 4/4-Takt (c) ein Relikt aus einer älteren Notationspraxis und steht für den 2/2-Takt.

74

A

Blockweises Lesen:
Bei rhythmisch parallelgeführten Stimmen.

B

C

D

Selektives
Lesen:
Man verfolgt
die führende
Stimme.

E

aus: Symphonie Nr. 4 B-Dur von Beethoven

A Durch die **Tempoangabe** (manchmal mit einer Metronomzahl verbunden) gibt der Komponist an, wie schnell ein Stück gespielt werden soll.

B Bei den Bläsern werden in der Regel zwei Stimmen in einer Notenzeile zusammengefasst. Spielen sie den gleichen Ton, erhält der Notenkopf zwei Hälse oder es steht a2 darüber.

C Zweistimmige Akkorde in den Notensystemen der Streicher werden von einem Spieler gespielt. Will man die Stimmen aufteilen, schreibt man **divisi** (geteilt). Dann spielt an jedem Pult ein Spieler die oberen und ein Spieler die unteren Noten.

D Hat eine Stimme, wie hier die Flöte, längere Zeit Pause, wird ihr Notensystem oft bis zum erneuten Einsatz der Stimme weggelassen. So wird Platz gespart, man muß weniger blättern und die erklingenden Stimmen sind übersichtlicher angeordnet.

E Um Platz zu sparen und Tonfolgen übersichtlicher zu gestalten, verwendet man gelegentlich sogenannte **Abbreviaturen (Faulenzer)**. Das hier verwendete Zeichen ♩ steht für ♪♪♪♪, wobei die Halbe Note die Dauer der Wiederholungen anzeigt und der Strich durch den Notenhals den Wert der zu wiederholenden Noten (1 Strich = Achtel, 2 = Sechzehntel usw.). Vgl. auch die Viola in T. 43, in der zunächst die Repetitionen ausgeschrieben und dann abgekürzt sind.

Partiturlesen im Klassensatz

Diese kurze Einführung können Sie als kostenloses Faltblatt bestellen – gern auch im Klassensatz!

Faltblatt "Die Kunst des Partiturlesens"
Bestellnummer: ETP 9999-99 (kostenlos)

Die passende Ergänzung für Klassen- und Unterrichtsräume:

Plakat A2 "Die Partitur im Überblick"
Bestellnummer ETP 9950-99 (kostenlos)

Mozart im Klassensatz

Ein Lebens- und Reisebild
Mozart war nicht nur einer der größten Komponisten, sondern auch einer der besten Pianisten des 18. Jahrhunderts. Wie heutige Virtuosen verbrachte er große Teile seines Lebens auf Konzertreisen zwischen den führenden Höfen und großen Städten seiner Zeit. Diese kleine Broschüre entfaltet ein Panorama des europäischen Musiklebens, das den Hintergrund für Mozarts Schaffen bildete. Eine Kurzbiographie und ein kleiner Einblick in seine Schreibweise runden das Bild ab.

Faltblatt "Mozart. Ein Lebens- und Reisebild"
Bestellnummer ETP 9990-99 (kostenlos)

Weitere Informationen unter www.eulenburg.de

Eulenburg